ADELE
The Complete Collection

Wise Publications
part of The Music Sales Group

London / New York / Paris / Sydney / Copenhagen / Berlin / Madrid / Hong Kong / Tokyo

Published by
Wise Publications
14-15 Berners Street, London W1T 3LJ, UK.

Exclusive Distributors:

Music Sales Limited
Distribution Centre,
Newmarket Road, Bury St Edmunds,
Suffolk IP33 3YB, UK.

Music Sales Pty Limited
4th floor, Lisgar House, 30-32 Carrington Street,
Sydney, NSW 2000, Australia.

Order No. AM1011802
ISBN 978-1-78558-290-5
This book © Copyright 2016 Wise Publications,
a division of Music Sales Limited.

Unauthorised reproduction of any part of
this publication by any means including photocopying
is an infringement of copyright.

Compiled & edited by Naomi Gibb.
Cover & prelims designed by Michael Bell Design.
Printed in the EU.

Your guarantee of quality:
As publishers, we strive to produce every book to
the highest commercial standards.
This book has been carefully designed to minimise awkward
page turns and to make playing from it a real pleasure.
Particular care has been given to specifying acid-free, neutral-sized paper
made from pulps which have not been elemental chlorine bleached.
This pulp is from farmed sustainable forests and was produced
with special regard for the environment.
Throughout, the printing and binding have been planned to
ensure a sturdy, attractive publication which should give years of enjoyment.
If your copy fails to meet our high standards, please inform us
and we will gladly replace it.

www.musicsales.com

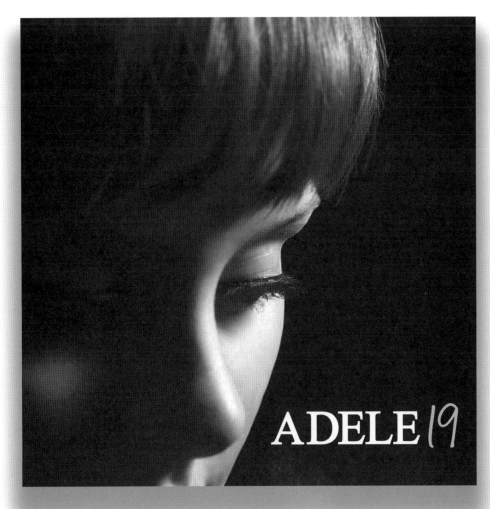

19

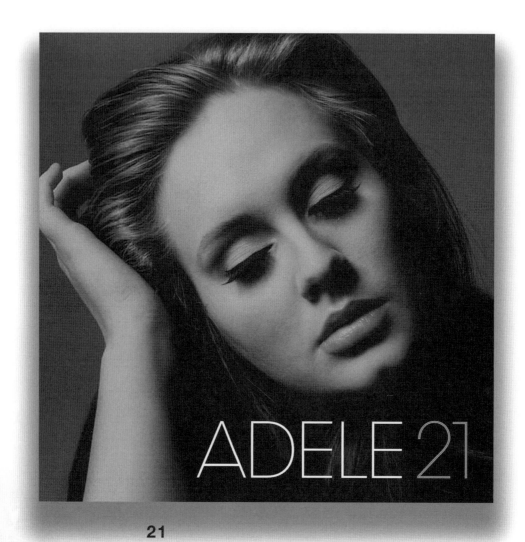

21

25

SKYFALL
from the Motion Picture *Skyfall* ... 225

SELECTED DISCOGRAPHY

ALBUMS

19
(2008)
XL Recordings CD XLCD313
Daydreamer
Best For Last
Chasing Pavements
Cold Shoulder
Crazy For You
Melt My Heart To Stone
First Love
Right As Rain
Make You Feel My Love
My Same
Tired
Hometown Glory

21
(2011)
XL Recordings CD XLCD520
Rolling In The Deep
Rumour Has It
Turning Tables
Don't You Remember
Set Fire To The Rain
He Won't Go
Take It All
I'll Be Waiting
One And Only
Lovesong
Someone Like You

iTunes Bonus Track:
I Found A Boy

UK, Poland & Bulgaria
Limited Edition Bonus Tracks:
Hiding My Heart
If It Hadn't Been For Love

Target Edition Bonus Tracks:
Need You Now
(live at CMT Artists Of The Year Awards)
Someone Like You (live acoustic)
Turning Tables (live acoustic)
Don't You Remember (live acoustic)

LIVE AT THE ROYAL ALBERT HALL
(2011)
XL Recordings Blu-Ray/CD XLBLU559
Hometown Glory
I'll Be Waiting
Don't You Remember
Turning Tables
Set Fire To The Rain
If It Hadn't Been For Love
My Same
Take It All
Rumour Has It
Right As Rain
One And Only
Lovesong
Chasing Pavements
I Can't Make You Love Me
Make You Feel My Love
Someone Like You
Rolling In The Deep
You, Me And Albert
(behind the scenes footage)

25
(2015)
XL Recordings CD XLCD740
Hello
Send My Love (To Your New Lover)
I Miss You
When We Were Young
Remedy
Water Under The Bridge
River Lea
Love In The Dark
Million Years Ago
All I Ask
Sweetest Devotion

Target Edition Bonus Tracks:
Can't Let Go
Lay Me Down
Why Do You Love Me

EPs

iTunes LIVE FROM SoHo
(2009)
XL Recordings CD XLCD5223F
Chasing Pavements
Crazy For You
Fool That I Am
Hometown Glory
Make You Feel My Love
Melt My Heart To Stone
Right As Rain
That's It, I Quit, I'm Movin' On

SINGLES

HOMETOWN GLORY
(2007)
XL Recordings CD
Hometown Glory
Best For Last

COLD SHOULDER
(2008)
XL Recordings CD XLS358CD
Cold Shoulder
Now And Then

**ADELE & THE RACONTEURS –
MANY SHADES OF BLACK**
(2008)
XL Recordings CD
Many Shades Of Black

CHASING PAVEMENTS
(2008)
XL Recordings CD XLS321CD
Chasing Pavements
That's It, I Quit, I'm Movin' On

MAKE YOU FEEL MY LOVE
(2008)
XL Recordings CD XLS393CD
Make You Feel My Love
Painting Pictures

ROLLING IN THE DEEP
(2010)
XL Recordings CD XLS521CD
Rolling In The Deep
If It Hadn't Been For Love

SOMEONE LIKE YOU
(2011)
XL Recordings CD
Someone Like You

SET FIRE TO THE RAIN
(2011)
XL Recordings CD
Set Fire To The Rain

SKYFALL
(2012)
XL Recordings CD XLS593CD
Skyfall
Skyfall (instrumental)

HELLO
(2015)
XL Recordings CD
Hello

WHEN WE WERE YOUNG
(2016)
XL Recordings CD
When We Were Young

ADELE
The Complete Collection

All I Ask

Words & Music by Adele Adkins, Bruno Mars,
Philip Lawrence & Christopher "Brody" Brown

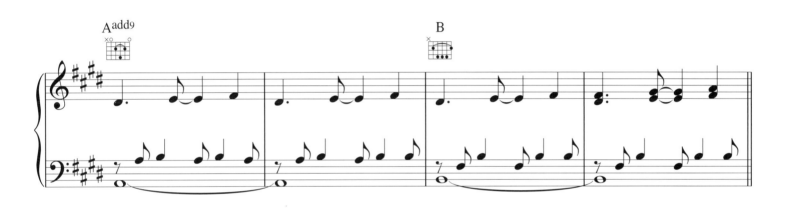

1. I will leave_ my heart at the door,_ I won't
2. I don't need_ your hon - es - ty,___ it's al-read-y in_

© Copyright 2015 Melted Stone Publishing Limited / WB Music Corporation / Mars Force Music /
Westside Independent Music Publishing LLC / Thou Art The Hunger / BMG Gold Songs / ZZR Music LLC / Late 80s Music.
Universal Music Publishing Limited / BMG Rights Management (US) LLC / Warner / Chappell North America Limited.
All Rights Reserved. International Copyright Secured.

9

use,_____ take me by_ the hand_ while_ we

do_____ what lov - ers_____ do, it mat-ters how_ this ends._

'Cause what if I nev-er love_____ a - gain?_

what if I nev-er love_____ a - gain?_

12

Best For Last

Words & Music by Adele Adkins

© Copyright 2007 Melted Stone Publishing Limited.
Universal Music Publishing Limited.
All Rights Reserved. International Copyright Secured.

on now,___ I'm try - ing to tell you just___ how I'd like___ to hear the words___ roll out___
think that___ I know___ things may nev - er change.___ But I'm___ still

___ of your mouth fi - nal - ly. Say that it's al - ways___ been___ me that's made you
hop - ing one___ day I___ might hear you say... I make you

♩ = 80 a tempo

D   Em   D/F♯   G

feel a way you've nev - er felt___ be - fore.___ And I'm

1° R.H. tacet till*

D   Em   D/F♯   G

all you need_____ and that you'd nev - er want_____ more.___ Then

you'd say all of the right things with-out a clue.

But you'd save the best for last like,___ I'm the one for you. You should

know that___ you're just a___ tem-po-rar-y fix. This is not

root-ed___ with you, it don't mean that much to me. You're_ just a

1.
Free time
N.C.

2. Why_____ is it ev - 'ry - time I think I've tried_____ my hard - est

it turns out it ain't e - nough? You're still not men - tion - ing_____ love. What am

I sup - posed_ to do to make_ you want_ me prop - 'ly? I'm

2.
Free time
N.C.

But_____ de - spite_____ the truth that I know, I find_____ it hard to

let go and give up on you. Seems I love the things you do, like the

a tempo

mean - er___ you treat me,___ more ea - ger___ I am to per -

-sist with__ this heart- break__ of run - ning__ a - round._____ And I

will do__ un - til I___ find__ my - self with you and make you

Can't Let Go

Words & Music by Adele Adkins & Linda Perry

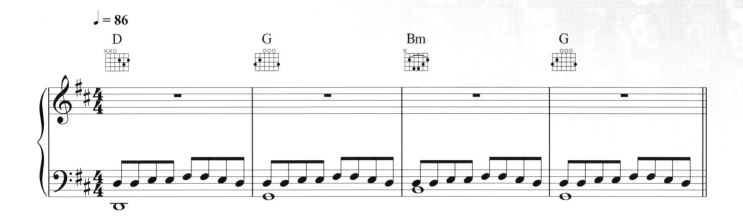

When did it___ go wrong?___ I will nev - er know.__ I have loved you all___

___ my life. How did it___ slow down?___ I go round__ and a - round,__

© Copyright 2015 Melted Stone Publishing Limited / Sony / ATV Melody / My Beloved Songs.

Universal Music Publishing Limited / Famous Music Corporation.

All Rights Reserved. International Copyright Secured.

D.S. al Coda

but a-you still went for___ the kill.___ I gave you hea-ven on a plat-ter, ba - by, I gave you ev-'ry-thing you

nev-er gave_ me. I nev-er lied and I nev-er faked_ it, on-ly want-ed for you to save___ me.

Coda

___ let go? Ooh_____ Some-times___ I feel like

___ I'm___ in the dark,___ ooh_____ I

Chasing Pavements

Words & Music by Adele Adkins & Eg White

© Copyright 2007 Kobalt Music Services Limited / Melted Stone Publishing Limited.
Universal Music Publishing Limited / Kobalt Music Publishing Limited.
All Rights Reserved. International Copyright Secured.

Cold Shoulder

Words & Music by Adele Adkins & Sacha Skarbe

© Copyright 2007 Melted Stone Publishing Limited.
Universal Music Publishing Limited.
All Rights Reserved. International Copyright Secured.

Crazy For You

Words & Music by Adele Adkins

1. Found my-self to-day sing-ing out loud your name. You said,
4. Late-ly with this state I'm in I can't help my-self but spin. I

I'm cra - zy. If I am, I'm cra-zy for
wish you'd come o - ver, send me spin-ning clos - er to

© Copyright 2007 Melted Stone Publishing Limited.
Universal Music Publishing Limited.
All Rights Reserved. International Copyright Secured.

Verse 5:
My, oh my, how my blood boils,
It's sweetest for you.
It strips me down bare
And gets me into my favourite mood.

Verse 6:
I keep on trying,
I'm fighting these feelings away.
But the more I do,
The crazier I turn into.

Daydreamer

Words & Music by Adele Adkins

© Copyright 2007 Melted Stone Publishing Limited.
Universal Music Publishing Limited.
All Rights Reserved. International Copyright Secured.

for.

But I will find him_____ sit - ting on my

door - step,_____ wait - - -

- ing____ for_____ a sur - prise.

Don't You Remember

Words & Music by Adele Adkins & Daniel Wilson

1. When will I see you again? You left with
2. When was the last time that you thought of me? Or have you com-

© Copyright 2010 Melted Stone Publishing Limited / Sugar Lake Music / BMG Monarch.

Universal Music Publishing Limited / Chrysalis Music Limited.

All Rights Reserved. International Copyright Secured.

wond-'ring eye____ and a heav-i-ness in my____ head.____ But don't you re-

-mem - ber?_____ Don't you re-

-mem - ber_____ the rea-son you loved me____

_____ be - fore? Ba - by, please re - mem -

First Love

Words & Music by Adele Adkins

© Copyright 2007 Melted Stone Publishing Limited.

Universal Music Publishing Limited.

All Rights Reserved. International Copyright Secured.

Fool That I Am

Words & Music by Floyd Hunt

© Copyright 1946 (Renewed) Chappell & Co., Inc.
Carlin Music Corporation.
All Rights Reserved. International Copyright Secured.

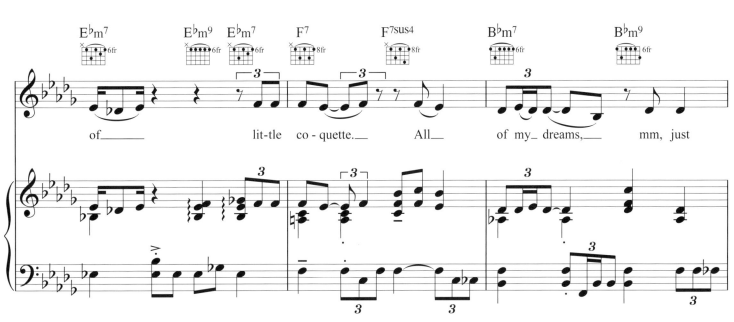

He Won't Go

Words & Music by Adele Adkins & Paul Epworth

© Copyright 2011 Melted Stone Publishing Limited.
Universal Music Publishing Limited / EMI Music Publishing Limited.
All Rights Reserved. International Copyright Secured.

pe - tri - fied,___ I'm so scared to step in - to this ride.___ What if I lose my heart and

fail to climb?_ I won't for-give me if I give up try - ing. 4. I heard his

2.

I'm will-ing to take___ the risk.___ There will__ be__

times___ we'll try and give it up,___ burst - ing at the

Hello

Words & Music by Greg Kurstin & Adele Adkins

© Copyright 2015 Melted Stone Publishing Limited / Kurstin Music / EMI April Music Inc.
Universal Music Publishing Limited / EMI Music Publishing Limited.
All Rights Reserved. International Copyright Secured.

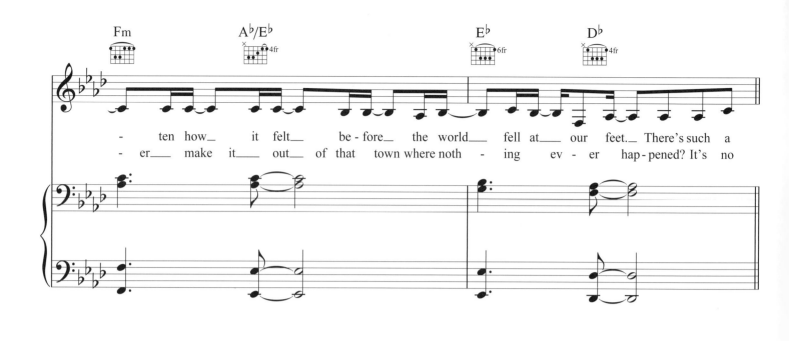

- ten how___ it felt___ be - fore___ the world___ fell at___ our feet.___ There's such a
- er___ make it___ out___ of that town where noth - ing ev - er hap - pened? It's no

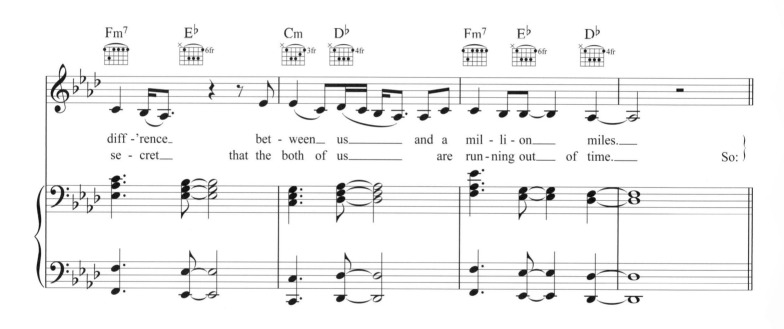

diff -'rence___ bet - ween___ us_____ and a mil - li - on___ miles.___
se - cret___ that the both of us_____ are run - ning out___ of time.___ So:

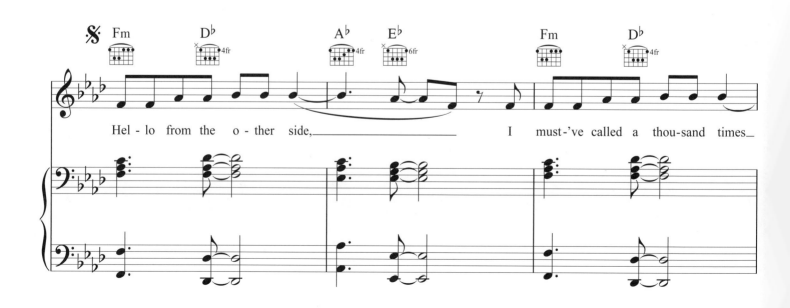

Hel - lo from the o - ther side,_____ I must -'ve called a thou - sand times___

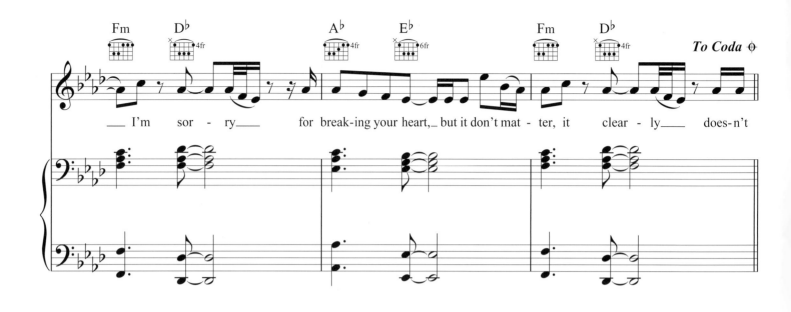

I'm sor - ry for break-ing your heart, but it don't mat - ter, it clear - ly does-n't

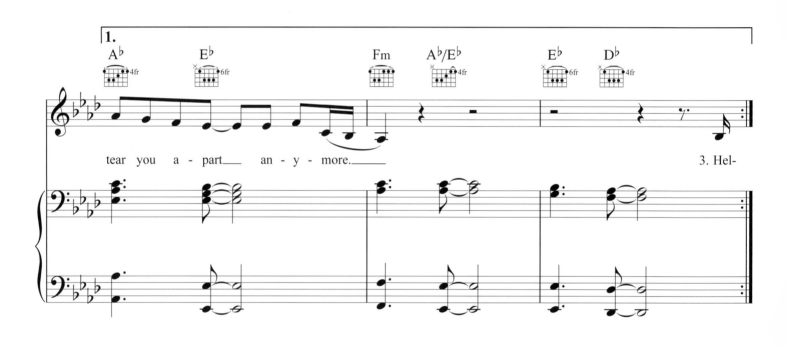

1.

tear you a - part an - y - more.

3. Hel-

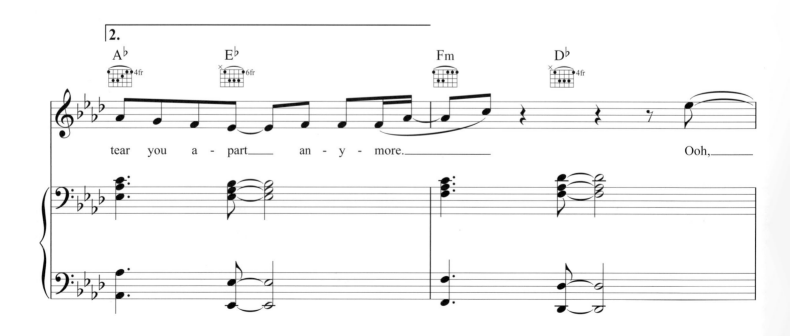

2.

tear you a - part an - y - more.

Ooh,

Hiding My Heart

Words & Music by Timothy Jay Hanseroth

© Copyright 2008 Southern Oracle Music LLC, USA.
Warner/Chappell North America Limited.
All Rights Reserved. International Copyright Secured.

79

I Can't Make You Love Me

Words & Music by Mike Reid & Allen Shamblin

1. Turn down the lights,_____ Turn down___ the bed;___
2. I close my eyes,_____ 'cause then I don't___ see___ the

turn down these voic - es in - side___ my head.___
love you don't feel_____ when you're hold - ing me.___

© Copyright 1991 Brio Blues Music / Almo Music Corporation / Universal Music MGB Songs.

Universal Music Publishing Limited / Rondor Music (London) Limited.

All Rights Reserved. International Copyright Secured.

Lay down with me,_____ and tell me no___ lies;___ just hold me close - ly,
Morn - ing will come,_____ and I'll do what's right.___ Just give me till then_____ to

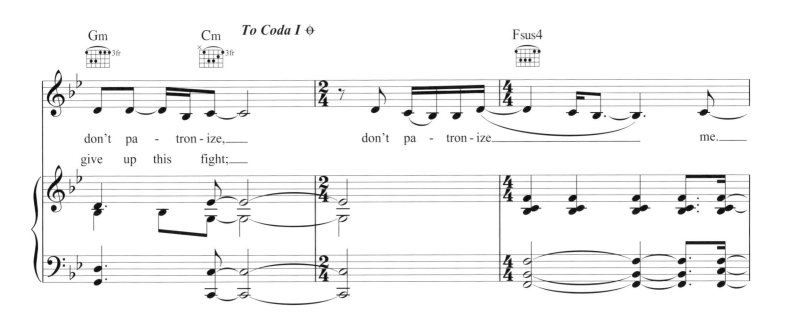

To Coda I ⊕

don't pa - tron - ize,___ don't pa - tron - ize_____ me.___
give up this fight;___

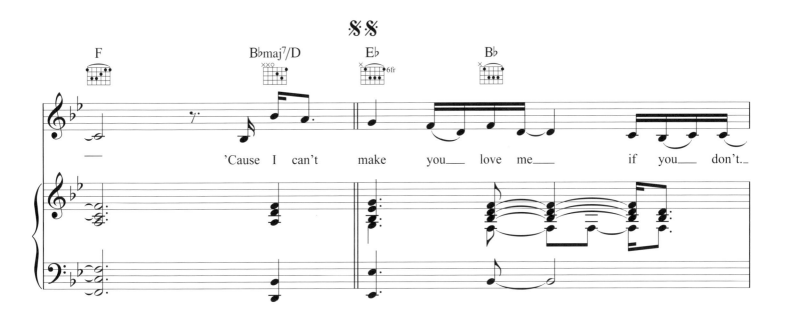

𝄋 𝄋

'Cause I can't make you___ love me_____ if you___ don't.__

And you can't make your heart feel something that it won't. And

here in the dark, these fi - nal hours, I will lay down my heart;

I will feel the pow - er, but you won't, no you won't. 'Cause I can't

make you love me when you don't, when you don't. (Ad lib. vocal)

To Coda II

Hometown Glory

Words & Music by Adele Adkins

© Copyright 2007 Melted Stone Publishing Limited.
Universal Music Publishing Limited.
All Rights Reserved. International Copyright Secured.

oh,_____ the peo - ple I've__ met_____ are the

won - ders of my_____ world, are the won - ders of my_____

_____ world, are the won - ders of this_____ world,_____ are the

won - ders_____ of now._____ 2. I ——

I Found A Boy

Words & Music by Adele Adkins

© Copyright 2010 Melted Stone Publishing Limited.
Universal Music Publishing Limited.
All Rights Reserved. International Copyright Secured.

I Miss You

Words & Music by Adele Adkins & Paul Epworth

© Copyright 2015 Melted Stone Publishing Limited.
Universal Music Publishing Limited / EMI Music Publishing Limited.
All Rights Reserved. International Copyright Secured.

teach you things you nev - er___ knew,___ ooh___ ba - by. Bring the floor up to my___ knees,___
no one has me like you__ do,___ ooh___ ba - by. Bring your heart, I'll bring my___ soul

___ let me fall in - to your gra - vi - ty.___ Then
___ but be de - li - cate with my e - go.___ I want to

kiss me back to life to___ see___ your bod - y stand - ing o - ver___ me.___
step in - to your great un - known,___ with you and me set - ting the___ tone.___

N.C.

Ba-by don't let the lights go down, ba - by don't let the lights go
(Lights go down, lights go down,

down

lights go down.)

Ba - by don't let the lights go down, lights go down, lights go

(Lights go down, down,_____

down, lights go down, lights go down,_____ down,_____ down._____ I

down.)_____

N.C.

miss you when the lights go out, it il - lu - mi-nates all of my doubts.

Pull me in,_____ hold me tight,_____ don't let go_____ ba - by give me light._____ I

(Pull me in,_____ hold me tight,_____ don't let go,_____ give me light.)_____

103

To Coda ⊕

miss you___ when the lights go out, it il - lu - mi-nates all of my doubts.__

Pull me in,___ hold me tight,___ don't let go,___ ba - by give me light.__ 𝄋 (I)
(Pull me in,___ hold me tight,___ don't let go,___ give me light.)

1.

2. I

Coda

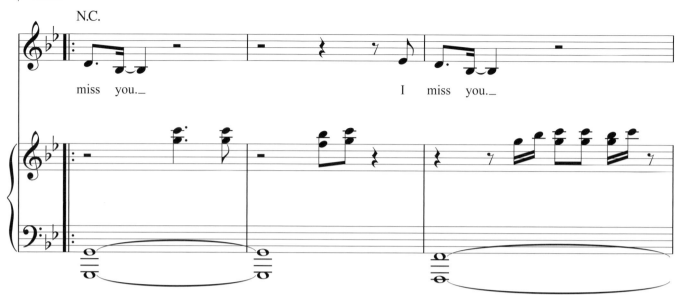

miss you.____   I   miss   you.____

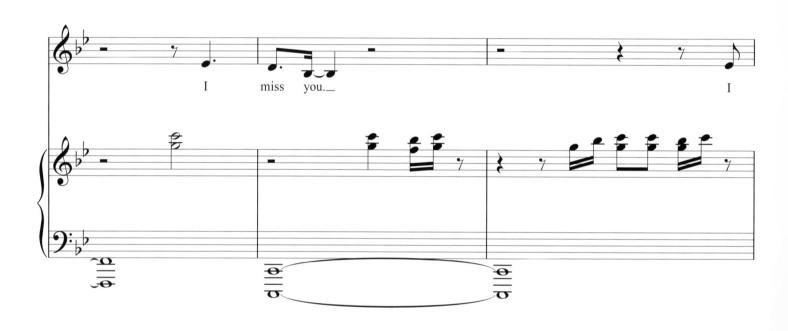

I   miss   you.____   I

Repeat ad lib.

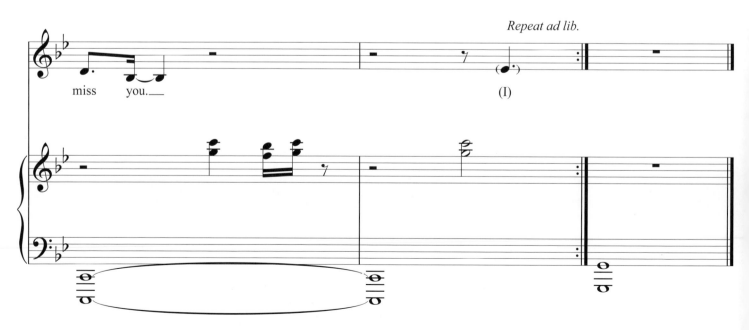

miss   you.____   (I)

Lay Me Down

Words & Music by Adele Adkins & Tobias Jesso

1. I would nev-er lie to you, un-less you tell
(2.) break the rules, un-less you tell

me to.
me to.

Ev - 'ry part of me,
You can read my mind,

© Copyright 2015 Melted Stone Publishing Limited / Songs Of Universal Inc.
Universal Music Publishing Limited / Universal / MCA Music Limited.
All Rights Reserved. International Copyright Secured.

If It Hadn't Been For Love

Words & Music by
Christopher Stapleton & Michael James Henderson

1. Nev-er would have hitch-hiked to Bir-ming-ham if it had-n't been for love.

I nev-er would have caught the train to Lou-'si-an - a if it

© Copyright 2004 Chicken Shack Songs / New Sea Gayle Music / Son Of A Miner Songs

Rondor Music (London) Limited / Kobalt Music Publishing Limited / Words and Music Inc.

All Rights Reserved. International Copyright Secured.

I'll Be Waiting

Words & Music by Adele Adkins & Paul Epworth

© Copyright 2011 Melted Stone Publishing Limited.
Universal Music Publishing Limited / EMI Music Publishing Limited.
All Rights Reserved. International Copyright Secured.

Love In The Dark

Words & Music by Adele Adkins & Samuel Dixon

1. Take____ your____ eyes____ off of me so I can leave,____ I'm
2. You____ have giv - en me some - thing that I can't live with - out,____ you

far____ too a - shamed to do it with you watch - ing me.
must - n't un - der - es - ti - mate that when you are in doubt. But

© Copyright 2015 Melted Stone Publishing Limited.
Universal Music Publishing Limited / BMG Rights Management (UK) Limited.
All Rights Reserved. International Copyright Secured.

love you_____ in the dark,_____ it feels like_ we're

o - ceans_____ a - part._____ There is so_

___ much space bet - ween___ us, ba - by, we're al - read - y de - feat - ed, yeah,_____

ev - 'ry - thing changed me.

126

D.S. al Coda

That's why I can't

Coda

And I

slow

— don't think you___ can save me.

128

Lovesong

Words by Robert Smith
Music by Robert Smith, Simon Gallup, Laurence Tolhurst,
Porl Thompson, Boris Williams & Roger O'Donnell

1. When-ev - er I'm____ a - lone___ with you
2. When-ev - er I'm____ a - lone___ with you

© Copyright 1989 Fiction Songs Limited.
Universal Music Publishing International MGB Limited.
All Rights Reserved. International Copyright Secured.

you make me feel___ like I am home a - gain.___
you make me feel___ like I am young a - gain.___

When - ev - er I'm___ a - lone___ with you
When - ev - er I'm___ a - lone___ with you

you make me feel___ like I am whole a - gain.___
you make me feel___ like I am fun a - gain.___

How - ev - er far___ a - way,___ I will al -

132

Make You Feel My Love

Words & Music by Bob Dylan

© Copyright 1997 Special Rider Music, USA.
All Rights Reserved. International Copyright Secured.

your case,____ I could of-fer you_ a___ warm em-brace____
your tears,____ I could hold_ you for__ a___ mil-lion_ years_____

1. to make you feel my love.____
2. to make you feel my love.__

I know you have-n't made your mind up yet,____ but I would nev-er do___ you wrong.__
The storms are rag-ing on the roll-ing sea, and on the high-way of re-gret___

I've known it from the mo-ment that we___ met;___
the winds of change are blow-ing wild and free;___

Melt My Heart To Stone

Words & Music by Adele Adkins & Francis White

© Copyright 2007 Melted Stone Publishing Limited / Kobalt Music Services Limited.
Universal Music Publishing Limited / Kobalt Music Publishing Limited.
All Rights Reserved. International Copyright Secured.

Million Years Ago

Words & Music by Adele Adkins & Greg Kurstin

© Copyright 2015 Melted Stone Publishing Limited / Kurstin Music / EMI April Music Inc.
Universal Music Publishing Limited / EMI Music Publishing Limited.
All Rights Reserved. International Copyright Secured.

not the on - ly one_____ who re - grets_____ the things they've done._____

_____ Some-times I_____ just feel it's on - ly me_____ { who can't stand the_____ re - / who nev - er_____ be -

-flec - tion that they see.) I wish I_____ could live a lit-tle more,_____ look up to_____ the
-came who they thought they'd be.)

sky, not_____ just the floor._____ I feel like_____ my life is flash-ing by_____ and all I_____ can

Many Shades Of Black

Words & Music by Jack White & Brendan Benson

1. Go a-head, go a-head and smash it on_____ the floor._____
2. Let it out, let it all out and say what's on your mind._____ You can

© Copyright 2008 Gladsad Music / Third String Tunes, USA / BMG Gold Songs.
EMI Music Publishing Limited / BMG Rights Management (US) LLC.
All Rights Reserved. International Copyright Secured.

150

My Same

Words & Music by Adele Adkins

© Copyright 2007 Melted Stone Publishing Limited.
Universal Music Publishing Limited.
All Rights Reserved. International Copyright Secured.

155

Need You Now

Words & Music by Josh Kear, Hillary Scott, David Haywood & Charles Kelley

1. Pic-ture per-fect mem-'ries   scat-tered all a-round the floor.__

(2.) -oth- er shot of whis-key,   can't stop look-ing at   the door.__

© Copyright 2009 Warner Tamerlane Publishing Corporation / Dwhaywood Music /
Radiobulletspublishing / Hillary Dawn Songs /EMI Foray Music/Year Of The Dog Music.
EMI Music Publishing Limited / Warner / Chappell North America Limited / International Dog Music.
All Rights Reserved. International Copyright Secured.

Reach-in' for the phone 'cause I can't fight it an - y - more.___

Wish-ing you'd come sweep - ing in the way you did be - fore.___

And I won - der if___ I ev - er cross___ your mind?___

___ For me it hap - pens all___ the time.___ It's a

quar - ter af - ter one, I'm___ all a - lone and I need___ you now.___ Said___

2º I'm___ a lit - tle drunk

I would-n't call but I lost___ all con-trol and I need__ you now.___

And I don't__ know how_ I can do__ with-out.___ I_____ just need_ you now._

1.

2. An -

Guess I'd ra- -ther hurt___ than feel___ noth - in'___ at all.___ It's a

just need you now.

Vocal ad lib.

Now And Then

Words & Music by Adele Adkins

© Copyright 2008 Melted Stone Publishing Limited.
Universal Music Publishing Limited.
All Rights Reserved. International Copyright Secured.

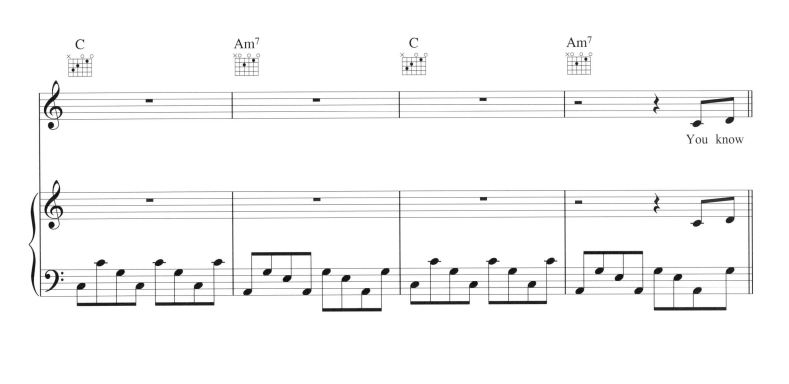

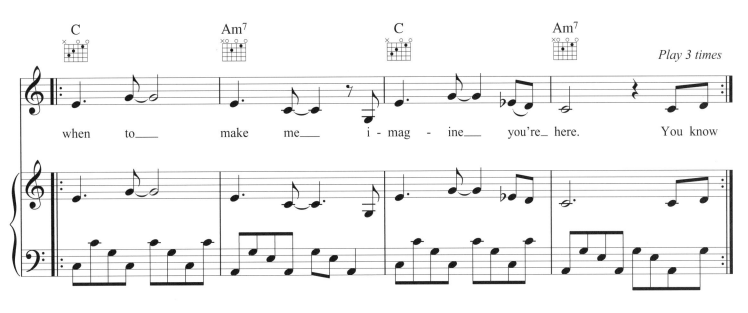

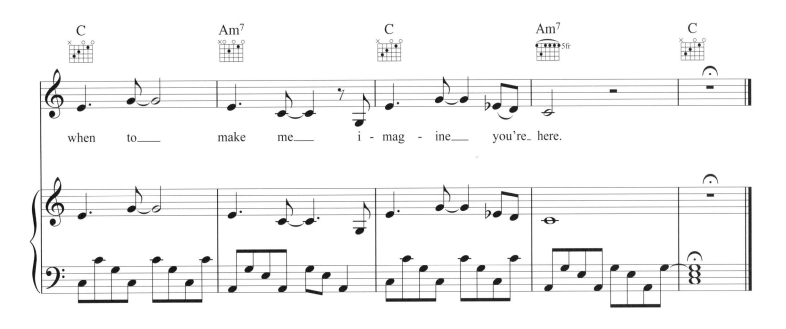

One And Only

Words & Music by Adele Adkins, Greg Wells & Daniel Wilson

© Copyright 2010 Melted Stone Publishing Limited / Firehouse Cat Music / Sugar Lake Music / BMG Monarch.
Universal Music Publishing Limited / Chrysalis Music Limited / BMG Rights Management (US) LLC.
All Rights Reserved. International Copyright Secured.

for-give your past_ and sim-ply be mine._____ I dare you to___

let me be___ your, your one and on - ly. Prom-ise I'm___

wor - thy to hold in your arms.___ So come on_____ and give_

me the chance___ to prove I am the one who can___ walk that

170

mile___ un-til the end starts. 2. Have I been on your

I know___ it ain't eas - y,___ giv-ing up___ your heart.___

Painting Pictures

Words & Music by Adele Adkins

1. Paint-ing pic-tures with my mind, mak-ing mem-o-ries

© Copyright 2008 Melted Stone Publishing Limited.
Universal Music Publishing Limited.
All Rights Reserved. International Copyright Secured.

Fill - ing up my heart with gold - en_____ stor - ies._____

Right As Rain

Words & Music by Adele Adkins,
Leon Michels, Jeff Silverman, Clay Holley & Nick Movshon

1. Who wants to be right as rain? It's bet-ter when some-thing
2. Who wants to be rid-ing high when you just crum-ble back
(3.) who wants to be right as rain? It's bet-ter when some-thing

— is wrong. You get ex-cite-ment in your bones and ev-
— on down? You give up ev-'ry-thing you are and e-
— is wrong. I get ex-cite-ment in my bones e-ven

© Copyright 2008 Melted Stone Publishing Limited / Songs Of The Fourmula / Kobalt Music Publishing America, Inc.
Universal Music Publishing Limited / Kobalt Music Publishing Limited / EMI Music Publishing Limited.
All Rights Reserved. International Copyright Secured.

Remedy

Words & Music by Adele Adkins & Ryan Tedder

1. I re-mem-ber all of the things that I thought I want-ed to be._
2. No ri-ver is too wide or too deep for me to swim__ to

you.__ So des-p'rate to find a way out of my
Come what-ev-er, I'll be the shel-ter that

© Copyright 2015 Melted Stone Publishing Limited / Write Me A Song Publishing.
Universal Music Publishing Limited / Kobalt Music Publishing Limited.
All Rights Reserved. International Copyright Secured.

look and you__ will see that I_____ will be your re - me - dy. When the

world seems so cruel___ and your heart makes you feel like a fool,___ I

prom - ise you__ will see that I_____ will be, I_____ will be your re-me-dy.__

When the

River Lea

Words & Music by Adele Adkins & Brian Burton

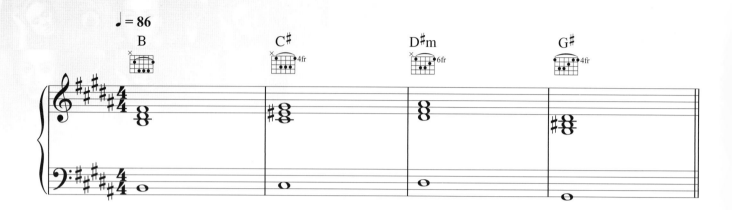

1. Ev - 'ry - bod - y tells__ me it's 'bout time that I moved on,__ that I

need to learn__ to light - en up__ and learn__ how to be young.__ But

© Copyright 2015 Melted Stone Publishing Limited / Sweet Science.
Universal Music Publishing Limited / Kobalt Music Publishing Limited.
All Rights Reserved. International Copyright Secured.

my heart is a val - ley, it's so shal - low and man - made,_ I'm

scared to death_ if I let you in____ that you'll see I'm just a fake.___

(1.) Some-times I feel lone - ly in the arms____ of your touch, but I

2. I should prob - 'ly tell___ you now_ be - fore___ it's way too___ late, that I

know that's_ just me_ 'cause noth - ing ev - er is___ e - nough.__

nev - er meant_ to hurt_ you or lie___ straight to your face.___ Con-

Rolling In The Deep

Words & Music by Paul Epworth & Adele Adkins

© Copyright 2010, 2011 Melted Stone Publishing Limited.
Universal Music Publishing Limited / EMI Music Publishing Limited.
All Rights Reserved. International Copyright Secured.

203

204

Rumour Has It

Words & Music by Ryan Tedder & Adele Adkins

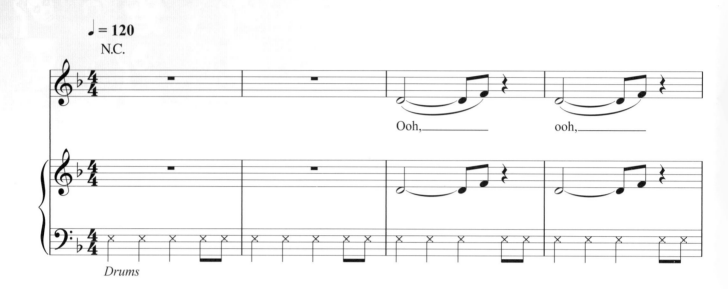

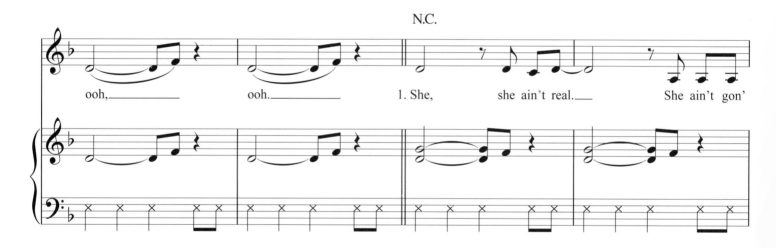

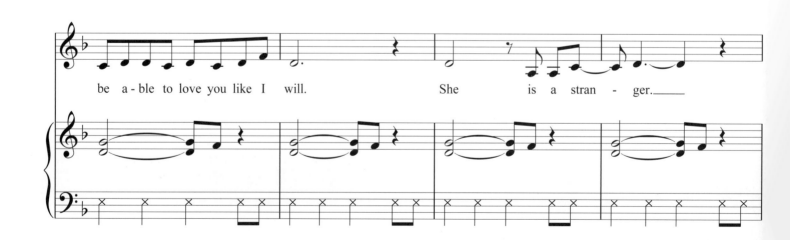

© Copyright 2010 Melted Stone Publishing Limited / Write 2 Live Publishing.
Universal Music Publishing Limited / Kobalt Music Publishing Limited.
All Rights Reserved. International Copyright Secured.

You and I have his-to-ry, or don't you re-mem-ber? Sure,_____ she's got it all._

_ But ba-by, is that real-ly what you want?_____

Dm

Gm⁷

Bless your soul you've got your head in the clouds. She's made a fool out-ta you_ and boy she's
You've made a fool out-ta me_ so boy I'm

Bᵇ

Dm/A

bring-ing you down._ She made your_ heart melt, but you're cold to the core._ Now
bring-ing you down._ You made my_ heart melt, yet I'm cold to the core._ But

209

Send My Love (To Your New Lover)

Words & Music by Adele Adkins, Max Martin & Shellback

© Copyright 2015 Melted Stone Publishing Limited / MXM Music AB.
Universal Music Publishing Limited / Kobalt Music Publishing Limited.
All Rights Reserved. International Copyright Secured.

1.
D5

2.
D

If you're read - y,___ if you're read - y,___ if you're read - y,___ I'm read - y.___

Bm

If you're read - y,___ if you're read - y,___ we both know we ain't kids no more.___

D5

No,___ we ain't kids no

Set Fire To The Rain

Words & Music by Fraser Smith & Adele Adkins

© Copyright 2010 Melted Stone Publishing Limited.
Universal Music Publishing Limited / Chrysalis Music Limited.
All Rights Reserved. International Copyright Secured.

Skyfall

Words & Music by Adele Adkins & Paul Epworth

8vb throughout

1. This is the end.___ Hold your breath and

count___ to ten. Feel the earth move and then

© Copyright 2012 Melted Stone Publishing Limited.
Universal Music Publishing Limited / EMI Music Publishing Limited.
All Rights Reserved. International Copyright Secured.

2.

Cm

- fall. (Let the sky fall. When it crum-bles we will stand tall.)

Cm(add9)   Cm

(Let the sky fall. When it crum-bles we will stand tall.)

Fm9   Ab6

Where you go I go, what you see I see. I know I'd

Eb/Bb   Ebaug/B   Cm   Abmaj9

nev-er be___ me___ with-out the se - cu - ri - ty___ of your lov-ing arms keep-ing

Someone Like You

Words & Music by Adele Adkins & Daniel Wilson

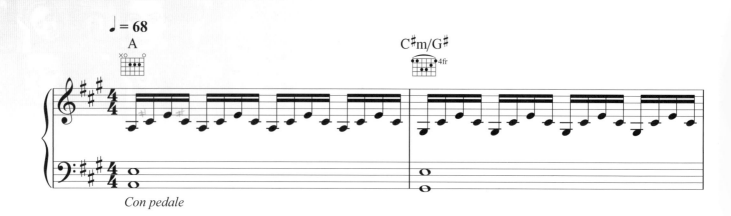

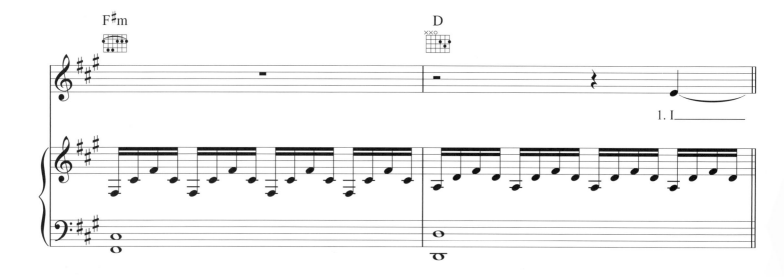

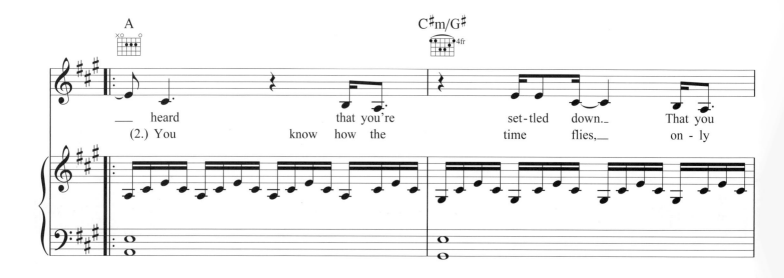

© Copyright 2010 Melted Stone Publishing Limited / Sugar Lake Music LLC / BMG Monarch.

Universal Music Publishing Limited / Chrysalis Music Limited.

All Rights Reserved. International Copyright Secured.

found a girl___ and you're mar-ried now._____ We were
yes - ter-day___ was the time of our lives.

I heard___ that your dreams came true. Guess she
born and raised___ in a sum - mer haze. Bound

gave you things___ I did-n't give to you._____ I
by the sur-prise of our glo - ry days.

1° only

Old friend, why are you so___ shy?_ Ain't like

you to hold back, or hide from the light. I
hate to turn up out of the blue un-in-vit-ed but I could-n't stay a-way. I could-n't fight it. I had
hoped you'd see my face and that you'd be re-mind-ed that for me it is-n't o - ver.

1° only

2° only

lasts and loves but some-times it hurts_ in - stead.

- stead.

Noth-ing com-pares, no wor-ries or cares, re-grets and mis-takes, they are mem-o-ries made.

Who would have known how bit-ter - sweet_ this would

235

Sweetest Devotion

Words & Music by Adele Adkins & Paul Epworth

1. With your

© Copyright 2015 Melted Stone Publishing Limited.
Universal Music Publishing Limited / EMI Music Publishing Limited.
All Rights Reserved. International Copyright Secured.

lov - ing there ain't noth - ing that I can't a - dore. The way I'm
(2.)-ev - er be what-ev - er you want me to be. I'd go

run - ning with you, hon - ey, means we can break ev - 'ry law. I find it
un - der and all o - ver for your cla - ri - ty. When you

fun - ny that you're the on - ly one I nev - er looked for. There is
won - der if I'm gon - na lose my way home, just re -

some-thing in your lov - ing that tears down my walls. } I weren't
-mem - ber that come what-ev - er I'll be yours all a - long.

239

know.

(The sweet - est, it's the sweet - est. The

sweet - est, it's the sweet - est. The sweet - est, it's the

sweet - est. The sweet - est, it's the sweet - est...) ...de - vo - tion.

Take It All

Words & Music by Adele Adkins & Francis Eg White

© Copyright 2010 Melted Stone Publishing Limited.
Universal Music Publishing Limited / BMG FM Music Limited - a BMG Chrysalis Company.
All Rights Reserved. International Copyright Secured.

too used to, well, hav-in' me 'round.___ Still, how can you walk a-way___ from all my___
bet-ter than this and this is ev-'ry-thing we need.___ So is it o-ver?___ Is this real-ly___

___ tears?___ It's gon-na be an emp-ty___ road with - out me right here.___ } But go on and
___ it? You're giv-in' up so eas-i-ly.___ I thought you loved me more than this, but go on...

take it,___ take it all___ with you.___

Tired

Words & Music by Francis White & Adele Adkins

Original key B major

♩ = 100

© Copyright 2007 Melted Stone Publishing Limited / Kobalt Music Services Limited.
Universal Music Publishing Limited / Kobalt Music Publishing Limited.
All Rights Reserved. International Copyright Secured.

should have known.

♩ = 100

Nev - er - mind, said your o - pen arms. I could - n't

help the leap that tripped me back in - to them. E - ven though I'm

D.S. al Coda

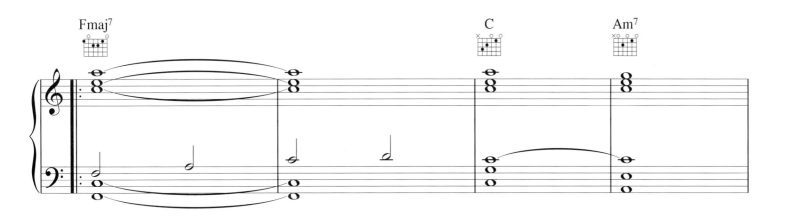
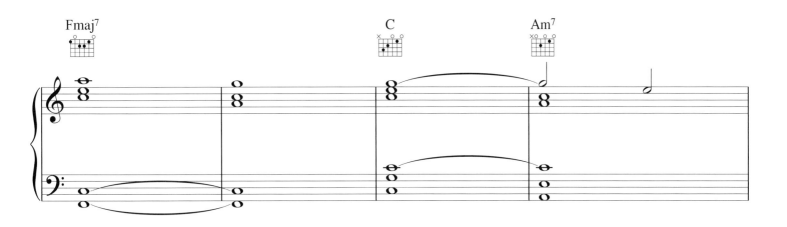
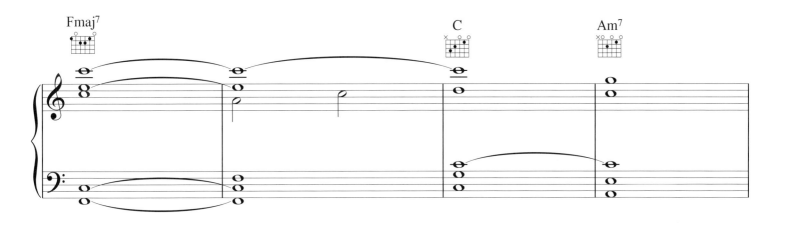
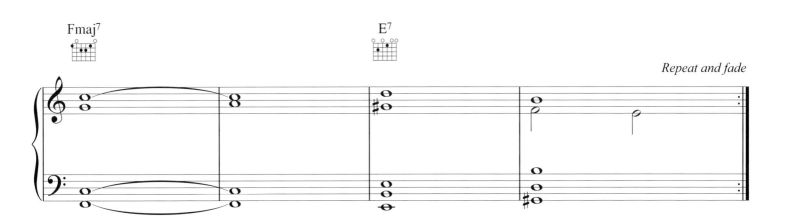

Turning Tables

Words & Music by Adele Adkins & Ryan Tedder

1. Close e-nough to start a war.
All that I

2. Un-der haunt-ed skies I see you.
Ooh.

© Copyright 2010 Melted Stone Publishing Limited / Write 2 Live Publishing.
Universal Music Publishing Limited / Kobalt Music Publishing Limited.
All Rights Reserved. International Copyright Secured.

Water Under The Bridge

Words & Music by Adele Adkins & Greg Kurstin

© Copyright 2015 Melted Stone Publishing Limited / Kurstin Music / EMI April Music Inc.
Universal Music Publishing Limited / EMI Music Publishing Limited.
All Rights Reserved. International Copyright Secured.

Say that our love ain't wa - ter un - der the

(Say it ain't so, say it ain't so.)

(Say it ain't so, say it ain't so.)

1.

bridge.

(Say it ain't so, say it ain't so.)

Whoa.

2.

bridge.

(Say it ain't so, say it ain't so.)

Say that our love ain't wa - ter un - der the bridge.

That's It, I Quit, I'm Movin' On

Words & Music by Roy Alfred & Del Serino

Country Blues ♩ = 146

1. When we used to say "good-night" I'd al-ways kiss and hold you tight, but late-ly you don't seem to care, you close the door and leave me

© Copyright 1961 (Renewed 1999) EMI Full Keel Music.
EMI Music Publishing Limited.
All Rights Reserved. International Copyright Secured.

got-ta go. Oh, that you know.

So, that's it, ba-by, I quit now, I'm mov-in' on.

So, that's it, ba-by, I quit now, I'm mov-in' on. "Brrr"

When We Were Young

Words & Music by Adele Adkins & Tobias Jesso

© Copyright 2015 Melted Stone Publishing Limited / Songs Of Universal Inc.
Universal Music Publishing Limited / Universal / MCA Music Limited.
All Rights Reserved. International Copyright Secured.

Why Do You Love Me

Words & Music by Adele Adkins & Richard Nowells

© Copyright 2015 Melted Stone Publishing Limited / R Rated Music.
Universal Music Publishing Limited / EMI Music Publishing Limited.
All Rights Reserved. International Copyright Secured.

shock in the dark that blew me a-way and you left___ your mark_ and it nev-er will fade. You ig-ni-

-ted a spark, let the fires a-way, are you rea-dy, rea-dy?_____ You have a

place in my heart that will al-ways be yours, you are the peak and dark of my un-i-verse. Ev-'ry piece_

___ and part,___ you were the first,___ I am rea-dy, rea-dy._____ It's a-

bove_____ and be-yond me, it's out_____ of my hands._____ Your

want_____ you. It's a-bove_____ and be-yond me, it's

out_____ of my hands. Your love_____ drives me cra-zy, it's

Repeat to fade

Also available from all good music shops...

AM1011373

AM1011340

AM993729

AM1003123

AM1009712

AM1011351

AM1011362

In case of difficulty
please contact:
Music Sales Limited
Newmarket Road,
Bury St Edmunds,
Suffolk, IP33 3YB, UK
www.musicsales.co